ROCK & POP

Female Voic
VO

CW00411201

7

TRINITY
COLLEGE LONDON

THE EXAM AT A GLANCE

For your Rock & Pop exam you will need to perform a set of **three songs** and one of the **Session skills** assessments, either **Playback** or **Improvising**. You can choose the order in which you play your set-list.

Song 1
Choose a song from this book

OR from www.trinityrock.com

Song 2
Choose a different song from this book

OR from www.trinityrock.com

OR perform a song you have chosen yourself: this could be your own cover version or a song you have written. It should be at the same level as the songs in this book. See the website for detailed requirements.

Song 3: Technical focus
Choose one of the Technical focus songs from this book, which cover three specific technical elements.

Session skills
Choose either **Playback** or **Improvising**.

When you are preparing for your exam please check on **www.trinityrock.com** for the most up-to-date information and requirements as these can change from time to time.

CONTENTS

Trinity College London's Rock & Pop syllabus and supporting publications have been devised and produced in association with Faber Music and Peters Edition London.

Trinity College London
Registered office:
89 Albert Embankment
London SE1 7TP UK
T + 44 (0)20 7820 6100
F + 44 (0)20 7820 6161
E music@trinitycollege.co.uk
www.trinitycollege.co.uk

Registered in the UK. Company no. 02683033
Charity no. 1014792
Patron HRH The Duke of Kent KG

Copyright © 2012 Trinity College London
First published in 2012 by Trinity College London

Cover and book design by Chloë Alexander
Brand development by Andy Ashburner @ Caffeinehit (www.caffeinehit.com)
Photographs courtesy of Rex Features Ltd
Printed in England by Caligraving Ltd

Audio produced, mixed and mastered by Tom Fleming
Backing tracks arranged by Tom Fleming
Musicians
Vocals: Alison Symons & Hannah Bridge
Keyboards: Dave Maric
Guitar: Tom Fleming
Bass: Ben Hillyard
Drums: George Double
Studio Engineer: Joel Davies www.thelimehouse.com

All rights reserved

ISBN: 978-0-85736-264-3

SONGS FIREWORK

Katy Perry
Words and Music by Katy Perry, Mikkel Eriksen, Tor Erik Hermansen, Sandy Wilhelm and Esther Dean

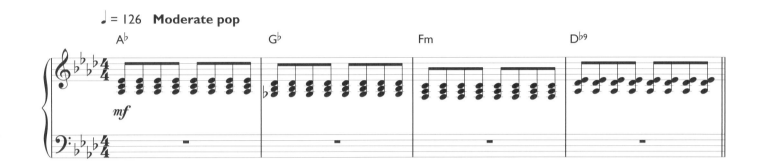

Do you ev-er feel like a plas-tic bag_____ drift-ing through the wind,

want-ing to start a-gain? Do you ev-er feel, feel so pa-per-thin,

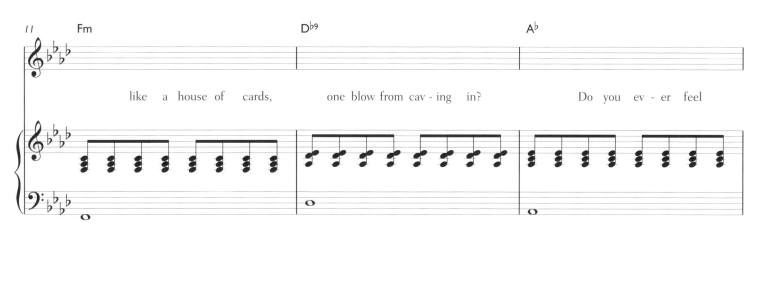

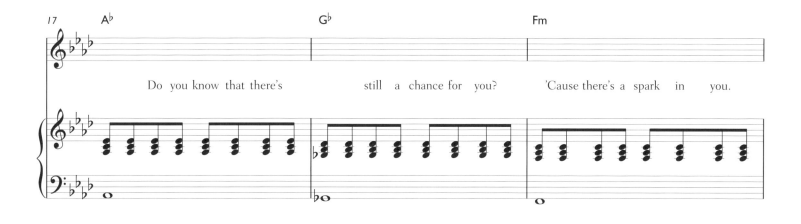

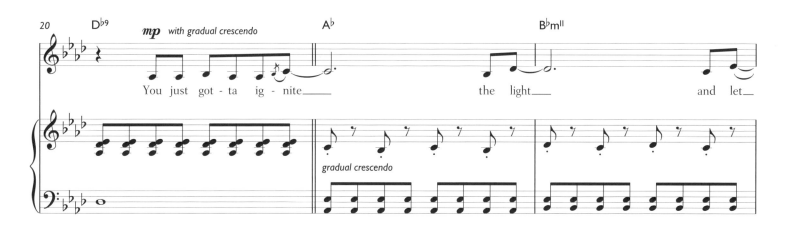

SONGS
WISHIN' ON A STAR

Rose Royce
Words and Music by Billie Calvin

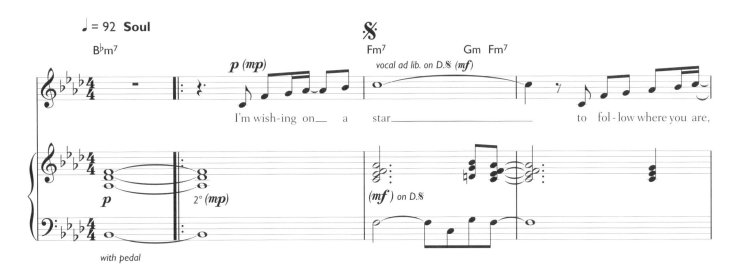

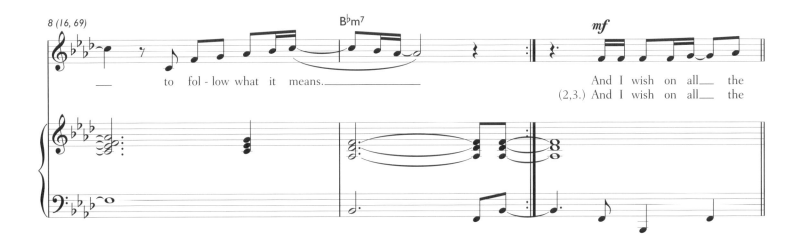

FEMALE VOICE GRADE 7

SONGS CAN'T FIGHT THE MOONLIGHT

LeAnn Rimes
Words and Music by Diane Warren

SONGS

I CLOSE MY EYES AND COUNT TO TEN

Dusty Springfield
Words and Music by Clive Westlake

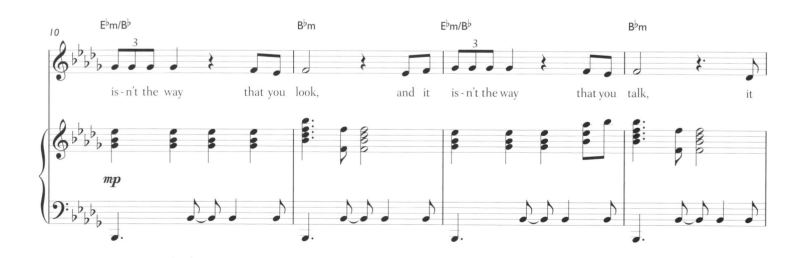

FREE MONEY

In your exam, you will be assessed on the following technical elements:

1 Different tone qualities

This song gives you the scope to explore a wide range of vocal tones and techniques. It starts at a gentle *piano*, where you can use a softer, warmer tone quality, but then, as the song increases in volume, you need to use a more edgy rock voice, with a stronger tone quality. After the spoken section, most of the remainder of the song is sung *forte* and *fortissimo*, so take good breaths between phrases and use plenty of support in order to maintain the volume and energy.

2 Spoken lyrics

In bars 52–59, the lyrics are spoken. They should be spoken confidently and with precise rhythms. Be ready for the triplets: all three notes should be the same length and they should flow evenly and sound natural. When you move from spoken voice back into the singing voice, make sure you can pitch the first note confidently.

3 Singing ad lib

There is an ad lib section in bars 120–127, using just the lyrics 'free money'. Practise singing these bars in a variety of ways – exploring different melodic, rhythmic and dynamic ideas – and decide what works best. Your ad lib needs to have a lot of energy and drive.

FREE MONEY

Patti Smith
Words and Music by Patti Smith and Leonard J Kaye

WITHOUT YOU

In your exam, you will be assessed on the following technical elements:

1 Melisma

There are several melismatic passages – where a group of notes is sung on one syllable. In bar 14, for example, the word 'go' is sung over five notes. Make sure you can pitch each note accurately at a slow tempo before gradually increasing the speed. Aim to move between the notes cleanly, without sliding over them.

2 Improvising

In the final chorus (bars 44–49), there is an opportunity for you to improvise. You should stay within the same feeling and style, basing your ideas on music from earlier in the song. Although the improvisation needs to sound spontaneous, it is a good idea to think about riffs and phrases which would work well in advance. Make sure that your performance has plenty of energy – leading to the final 'I can't give anymore'.

3 Advanced tone qualities

In this song there are opportunities to use more advanced vocal tone qualities. These can be used to heighten the emotional intensity of the song and could include:

- Belting – a vocal style used to produce a loud sound in the upper middle of the pitch range. This could be used from bar 36, for example. (Note that belting can cause strain to the vocal mechanism if not supported properly. Be careful not to strain by bringing the voice into a 'shouting' tone).
- On and off the breath – the chorus could be sung on the breath (with a focused and resonant sound) while the opening could be sung off the breath (with a breathy, wide sound).
- Sob quality – a lower-pitched, deep-voiced vibrato with a soft, dark tone, which could be used in, for example bars 4–9.

The examiner will expect you to use at least one of these techniques during the course of your performance.

WITHOUT YOU

Mariah Carey
Words and Music by Peter Ham and Thomas Evans

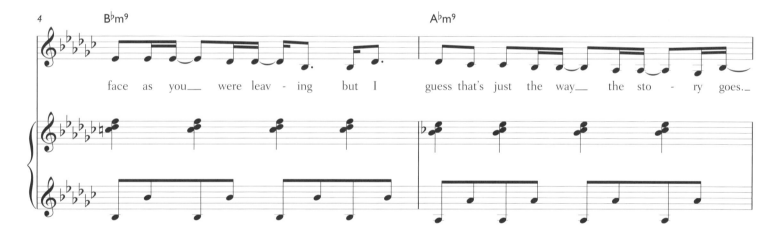

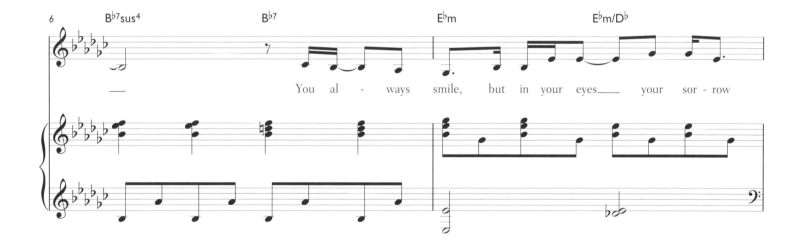

FIREWORK

Katy Perry

Katy Perry is a Californian singer. The daughter of two pastors, she made her musical debut in the local church choir. She started her music career as a Christian artist with a gospel music album. Following her reinvention as boisterous tongue-in-cheek pop star, she rose to prominence in 2008 with her album *One Of The Boys*. She is known for her unconventional dress sense and often uses fruit-shaped accessories as part of her wardrobe.

The catchy pop song 'Firework' is from her third studio album *Teenage Dream* (2010). The lyrics, co-written by Perry, are about self-empowerment. The video sees Perry in Budapest surrounded by shy teenagers who increasingly become more confident.

PERFORMANCE · HINTS & TIPS

This song needs to be performed in a strong and determined way. Articulate the consonants clearly – they give the song energy and enable the listener to understand you more easily.

The song starts with a vocal ad lib. Learn the notated part of the song first: once you are familiar with the song, you can start thinking about what you might do in the ad lib section. The pre-chorus (starting at bar 20) opens *mezzo piano* and gradually *crescendos* through to *forte* at the chorus. Use the *crescendo* and the gradually rising pitch to help convey a feeling of energy and anticipation. The chorus should be sung in a powerful voice, but not sound forced or shouted.

There are several large leaps in the melody of this song. Learn to recognise the sound of the different intervals and practise pitching them accurately so that they are in tune.

'You just gotta ignite the light'

WISHIN' ON A STAR

Rose Royce

The nine-piece collective Rose Royce originally got together in Los Angeles in the early 1970s as a multi-purpose backing group called Total Concept Unlimited. They auditioned for the soul singer Edwin Starr, who hired them as his backup band. Through Starr they met the legendary songwriter and Motown producer Norman Whitfield who signed them to his new label.

Renamed as Rose Royce, and with new lead singer Gwen Dickey in place, the band's first major success was with the film track to *Car Wash*, a new film for which Whitfield wrote the score. The film music turned out to be a huge success spawning several hits – not least the poignant 'Wishin' On A Star'. There have been many covers of the song, notably by Beyoncé and Seal. Gwen Dickey duetted with Jay Z on his version of the song in 1998.

Be careful with the pitching and timing of your first entry in this song: it comes just after the second beat of the bar (as do many of your entries). Your first note is the ninth of the chord – with practice you will start to hear this pitch naturally because it starts each phrase in the verses.

The only *forte* passage in this song is in the middle eight (starting at bar 42). For this section, try adding a stronger edge to your voice, to contrast with the softer, warmer tone qualities needed for the rest of the song. The repeated middle eight ends with a long held note. Ensure you take a good breath in preparation for this.

In the coda (starting at bar 78) you are given the opportunity to ad lib. You will need to stick to the lyrics, but you are free to pull the melody around as you wish. You could include some typical soul or gospel ad libs. Experiment with your voice, but remember to keep within the style of the song. The ad lib section must lead seamlessly into the final phrase of the song, which should be performed as written.

'In *the* game *of* love *you* reap *what* you *sow*'

CAN'T FIGHT THE MOONLIGHT

LeAnn Rimes

LeAnn Rimes was raised in Garland, Texas. As a young teenager she was already an experienced country singer, having won a national television talent competition, recorded three albums, and regularly performed 'The Star Spangled Banner' at the opening ceremonies of the Dallas Cowboys football games. Her big breakthrough came in 1996, when she was only 14, with her single 'Blue'. Throughout her career, Rimes' rich powerful vocals have been compared to those of the country singer Patsy Cline and she has covered many of Cline's songs.

'Can't Fight The Moonlight' was featured on the soundtrack of the film *Coyote Ugly*. It was written by the award-winning American songwriter Dianne Warren with production by the legendary Trevor Horn. In 2000, it was released as a single and enjoyed huge international success; it was later released as a maxi-single with several remixes.

There are several changes of key in this song. The vocal melody leads these key-changes so your pitching must be very secure. Take care with the accidentals that lead to the key changes, for example the E♭ in bar 17(42) and the B♮ in bar 28.

After the bridge section, the song modulates up a semitone (bar 66) – this gives the song an extra surge of energy. There is a brief ad lib on the word 'try' as you reach the new key. Make sure that you take a good breath for this: the ad lib should be lively and energetic, building towards the final chorus.

The melody line of this song spans nearly two octaves and includes several leaps. The melody line is often independent of the accompaniment: make sure that you can pitch all notes securely.

'Deep *in* the *dark,* you'll *surrender* your *heart*'

I CLOSE MY EYES AND COUNT TO TEN

Dusty Springfield

Dusty Springfield (1939–1999) was born Mary O'Brien. She began her career by singing with her brother Dion in The Springfields and then went on to have a long career as a solo singer. She had a distinctive, sultry sound rooted in black soul music – this led to her being dubbed the White Queen of Soul. With her trendy clothes, heavy eye make-up and peroxide blonde hair, she became a pop icon of the Swinging Sixties. Between 1964 and 1970 she was one of the most successful British female performers, with 18 singles in the charts.

The soulful love song 'I Close My Eyes And Count To Ten' (1968) became one of Dusty Springfield's bestselling singles.

The song opens and closes in B♭ minor but the key changes to B♮ major twice during the song. On both occasions it slows down ready for the key change and then goes back to the original speed. These passages need careful attention: you should be ready for the key changes and listen carefully to the other parts for the tempo changes.

This is a dramatic piece which requires much use of contrast. The opening instrumental introduction, for example, starts quite quietly, suddenly becoming very loud on the last note of bar 3. Make sure that you observe all the dynamic markings – the shading and contrast add a lot of character. Take care with the ⟩ on the long held notes (bar 59, for example). These will need good breath and tone control.

Be ready for the triplets in, for example, bars 20, 35 and 37. All three notes of the triplet should be the same length and they should flow evenly and sound natural, following the rhythm of the words.

'Somehow I can't believe it's true'

FREE MONEY

Patti Smith

Patti Smith was one of the trailblazers of the anarchic punk genre. Her creatively uncompromising music is hard to categorise, but could be loosely described as 'art rock'. She was hugely significant in changing the image of women in rock. The cover of her 1975 debut album *Horses* is a shot of Smith taken by the American photographer Robert Mapplethorpe. It shows her dressed in a simple white shirt and skinny tie with unkempt hair and a defiant expression. This potent image demonstrated her refusal to be objectified as a woman and paved the way for other women in pop.

'Free Money' is from her 1975 debut album *Horses* – an avant-garde album produced by ex-Velvet Underground member John Cale. *Horses* is an unconventional and innovative fusion of punk rock and stream-of-consciousness spoken poetry. Patti Smith's vocals on 'Free Money' have a typically anarchic spirit.

PERFORMANCE · HINTS & TIPS ·

'Free Money' is driven by the words. Speak the words in rhythm, with the track, before you sing the song: this will help you sing the rhythms accurately. Articulate the consonants clearly – they give the song energy and enable the listener to understand you more easily. In particular, work on your articulation on repeated lyrics such as the rapid repetition of 'free money' at the end of the song.

The melody line is often independent of the accompaniment so you will need to ensure that you can pitch all the notes securely and sing the syncopated rhythms accurately. There are vocal slides in bars 90 and 94–95: these need to sound natural and unforced.

'Those dollar bills go swirling round my bed'

WITHOUT YOU

Mariah Carey

Mariah Carey's story is one of rags to riches: from a difficult childhood to become one of the most successful female solo artists ever to top the charts in America. Unlike many of her peers, Carey writes most of her own songs. Love is a dominant theme in her lyrics and the songs are often influenced by gospel music.

Carey is well known for her wide vocal range and use of 'melisma' (where a group of notes is sung on one syllable). This vocally acrobatic style has become a defining element in the music of many of Carey's peers – such as Beyoncé and Christina Aguilera.

'Without You' is taken from one of Mariah Carey's most popular albums, *Music Box* (1994). It was originally written and recorded by the band Badfinger. The song was an international best seller for Harry Nilsson in 1972 and again for Carey in 1994. It has been covered by hundreds of artists and is a popular choice for television talent shows.

This emotional ballad has a wide range (two octaves) and you will need to move between different registers of the voice: make sure that your voice is thoroughly warmed up before singing it. The verses cover a smaller range and are sung at either *piano* or *mezzo piano*. The choruses use the full range and are sung louder. The final chorus is the loudest part of the song and you will need a lot of support and stamina to keep the volume and energy up.

In bars 9 and 28–35 you are given the opportunity to ad lib and put your personal mark on the song. Practise singing these bars in a variety of ways – exploring different melodic, rhythmic and dynamic ideas – and decide what works best. In verse 3 you are free to ad lib around the melody, but make sure that your vocal line still fits with the backing vocals.

'In *your* eyes *your* sorrow *shows*'

YOUR PAGE NOTES

SESSION SKILLS

PLAYBACK

For your exam, you can choose either Playback or Improvising (see page 50).
If you choose Playback, you will be asked to perform some music you have not seen or heard before.

In the exam, you will be given the song chart and the examiner will play a recording of the music. You will hear several four-bar to eight-bar phrases on the recording: you should sing each of them straight back in turn. There's a rhythm track going throughout, which helps you keep in time. There should not be any gaps in the music.

In the exam you will have two chances to perform with the recording:
- First time – for practice
- Second time – for assessment

You should listen to the audio, copying what you hear; you can also read the music. Here are some practice song charts which are also on the CD in this book.

The music is printed without text and may be sung to any vowel (with or without consonant) or to sol-fa. Some of the examples may include accents so you may need to use consonants or scat words for these to make them really obvious.

Don't forget that the Playback test can include requirements which may not be shown in these examples, including those from earlier grades. Check the parameters at www.trinityrock.com to prepare for everything which might come up in your exam.

'I really *like* the *way* music *looks* on *paper.* It *looks* like *art* to *me*'

Steve Vai

Practice playback 1

Practice playback 2

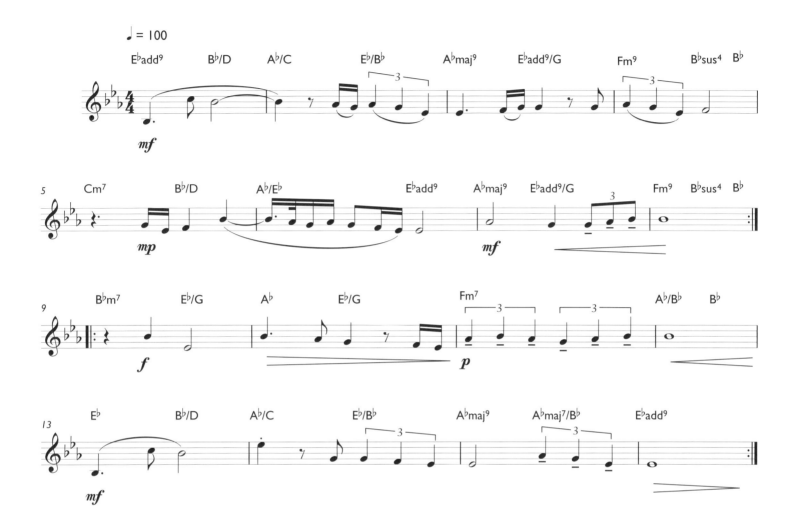

SESSION SKILLS IMPROVISING

For your exam, you can choose either Playback (see page 47), or Improvising. If you choose to improvise, you will be asked to improvise over a backing track that you haven't heard before in a specified style.

In the exam, you will be given a song chart and the examiner will play a recording of the backing track. The backing track consists of a passage of music played on a loop. You should improvise a melody line over the backing track.

In the exam you will have two chances to perform with the recording:
- First time – for practice
- Second time – for assessment

Here are some improvising charts for practice which are also on the CD in this book. You may improvise to any vowel (with or without consonant) or to sol-fa.

Don't forget that the Improvising test can include requirements which may not be shown in these examples, including those from earlier grades. Check the parameters at www.trinityrock.com to prepare for everything which might come up in your exam.

Practice improvisation 1

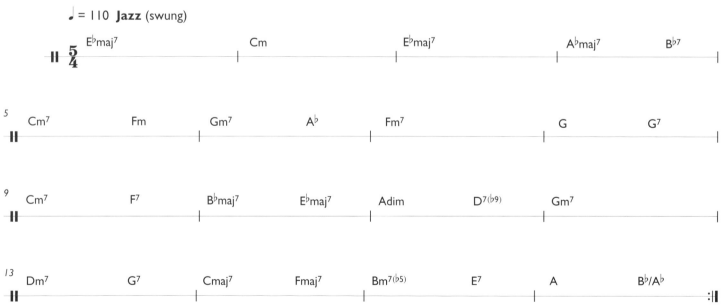

Practice improvisation 2

♩ = 140 **Boogie-style rock**

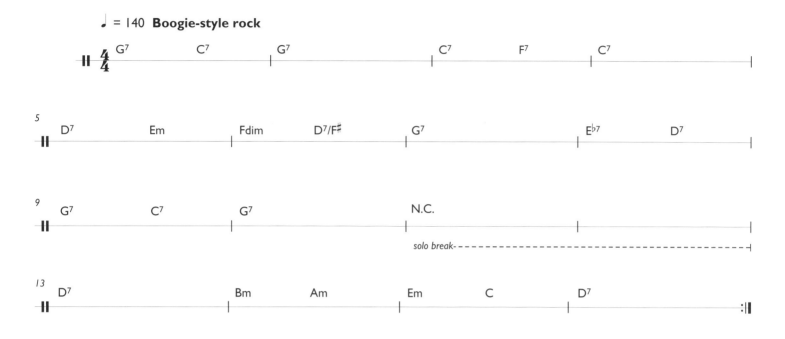

'Relax.
Enjoy yourself.
Play a lot.'

Joe Satriani

CHOOSING A SONG FOR YOUR EXAM

There are lots of options to help you choose your three songs for the exam. For Songs 1 and 2, you can choose a song which is:

- from this book
- from www.trinityrock.com

Or for Song 2 you can choose a song which is:

- sheet music from a printed or online source.
- your own arrangement of a song or a song you have written yourself.

You can perform the song unaccompanied or with a backing track (minus the solo voice). If you like, you can create a backing track yourself (or with friends).

For Grade 7, the song should last between two-and-a-half and four minutes, and the level of difficulty should be similar to your other songs. When choosing a song, think about:

- Does it work for my voice?
- Are there any technical elements that are too difficult for me? (If so, perhaps save it for when you do the next grade.)
- Do I enjoy singing it?
- Does it work with my other pieces to create a good set-list?

See www.trinityrock.com for further information and advice on choosing your own song.

SHEET MUSIC

For your exam, you must always bring an original copy of the book or download sheets with email certificate / proof of purchase for each song you perform in the exam. If you choose to write your own song you must provide the examiner with a copy of your music.

Your music can be:

- a lead sheet with lyrics, chords and melody line
- a chord chart with lyrics
- a full score using conventional staff notation

The title of the song and your name should be on the sheet music.

IMPROVISING IN SONGS

Improvisation is an exciting and creative way to make the music your own. Rock and pop music often includes opportunities for musicians to improvise during a song – this is a great way to display your instrumental/vocal skills and musical abilities. This might include singing your own melody line, ad-libbing around a given tune or making up an accompaniment.

Make sure you know the song well and feel comfortable and confident with the rhythms, chord progressions and the general groove that underpins the music. Once you're familiar with it, the best way to learn how to improvise is to do it!

Some useful starting points might be:

- Identify just a few notes that sound good over the chord progressions, and experiment with these first.
- Add more notes as your musical ideas start to develop – improvising is often most effective when a simple idea is repeated, varied and extended.
- You don't need to fill every gap! Silence can be an important – and very effective – part of your improvisation.
- The more you improvise – and experiment – the better you will become, until your improvisations seem effortless.

It's important to be aware of the tonality of the song and to recognise different scales and modes that are appropriate to use. Start by familiarising yourself with:

- the minor pentatonic scale
- the blues scale
- the Dorian mode
- major and minor scales

You might find it useful to listen to some original versions of different rock and pop songs. Have a go at learning some of the vocal solos – this will help you to develop an understanding of how other musicians develop musical material.

PERFORMING

Being well prepared is the secret of a good performance. The more you practise, the better you will perform.

Top Ten Practice Tips

1 Develop a regular practice routine. Try to set aside a certain amount of time every day.

2 Choose specific things to practise each week.

3 Set goals for each practice session and continually review your progress.

4 Sing a wide variety of songs – not just your favourites over and over again – to increase your skill and adaptability.

5 Identify the parts of the songs you find difficult and give them special attention.

6 Practise those techniques that you struggle with as well as those you find easier.

7 Don't reinforce mistakes by repeating them over and over again.

8 Include warm-ups and technical exercises in your practice sessions as well as songs.

9 Use a metronome.

10 Record yourself on audio or video. Listen to your older recordings to see how much you have improved.

Try to memorise the music – aim to sound free and natural and put your own stamp on the songs.

PERFORMING

BEFORE YOUR PERFORMANCE

- Watch and listen to others perform. Go to live performances and watch some videos online. Think about the aspects of performances you particularly like and try them out.
- Practise singing in front of an audience and communicate with them.
- Learn some relaxation and breathing exercises.
- Be positive about your performance. Think about how good your performance will be.
- Know your music.

ON THE DAY OF YOUR PERFORMANCE

- Wear something comfortable.
- Try some physical exercises.
- Warm up.
- Do some relaxation and breathing exercises.

THE PERFORMANCE

Your audience may be large or small – and in an exam may only be one person – but it is important to give a sense of performance no matter how many people are present.

- Walk into the room confidently.
- Keep your head up, so you can look at your audience and acknowledge them.
- Focus on the music.
- Look confident and keep going, no matter what happens.
- Engage with your audience.
- Enjoy yourself.

MICROPHONE TECHNIQUE

Here are some points to bear in mind when you use a mic in performance:

- Consider whether you are going to hold the mic or use a stand. If you use a stand, place it at a comfortable height so you don't have to bend over. Be aware of trailing leads.
- There should be about five to eight centimeters between your mouth and the mic – closer for quiet, breathy singing and further away for louder singing and powerful high notes.

- Experiment with different vocal sounds – whispering and shouting, high and low notes, vowels and consonants. Learn how to avoid hisses and pops. Depending on the mic you use, popping sounds can occur when singing P, B, T and D and hissing sounds with S and Z.
- Never point the mic towards a speaker or stage monitor – this will create feedback.

PLAYING WITH BACKING TRACKS

The CD contains demos and backing tracks of all the songs in the book. The additional songs at www.trinityrock.com also come with demos and backing tracks.

- In your exam, you can perform with the backing track or create your own.
- The backing tracks begin with a click track, which sets the tempo and helps you start accurately.
- Be careful to balance the volume of the backing track against your voice.
- Listen carefully to the backing track to ensure you are singing in time.

If you are creating your own backing track here are some further tips:
- Make sure the sound quality is of a good standard.
- Think carefully about the instruments/sounds you are putting on the backing track.
- Avoid copying what you are singing on the backing track – it should support not duplicate.
- Do you need to include a click track at the beginning?

COPYRIGHT IN A SONG

If you are a singer or songwriter it is important to know about copyright. When someone writes a song or creates an arrangement they own the copyright (sometimes called 'the rights') to that version. The copyright means that other people cannot copy it, sell it, perform it in a concert, make it available online or record it without the owner's permission or the appropriate licence. When you write a song you automatically own the copyright to it, which means that other people cannot copy your work. But just as importantly, you cannot copy other people's work, or perform it in public without their permission or the appropriate licence.

Points to remember
- You can create a cover version of a song for an exam or other non-public performance.
- You cannot record your cover version and make your recording available to others (by copying it or uploading it to a website) without the appropriate licence.
- You own the copyright of your own original song, which means that no one is allowed to copy it.
- You cannot copy someone else's song without their permission or the appropriate licence.
- If you would like to use somebody else's words in your own song you must check if they are in copyright and, if so, we recommend you confirm with the author that they are happy for the words to be used as lyrics.
- Materials protected by copyright can normally be used as lyrics in our examinations as these are private performances under copyright law. The examiner may ask you the name of the original author in the exam.
- When you present your own song to the examiner make sure you include the title, the names of any writers and the source of your lyrics.